What
is
True?

V L B | Veronica Lane Books

What is True?

By Etan Boritzer   Illustrated by Jeff Vernon

V L B | *Veronica Lane Books*

www.veronicalanebooks.com   email: etan@veronicalanebooks.com
2554 Lincoln Blvd. Ste 142, Los Angeles, CA 90291 USA
Tel/Fax: +1 (800) 651-1001 / Intl: +1 (310) 745-0162

Library of Congress Cataloging-In-Publication Data
        Boritzer, Etan, 1950-
        What Is True / by Etan Boritzer
        Illustrated by Jeff Vernon -- 1st Edition
        p. cm.

SUMMARY: Presents children with an understanding of concepts related to determining the various elements of truth.

Audience: Grades K - 6

ISBN 978-9762743-0-2 (Hardbound)
ISBN 978-9762743-1-9 (Paperback)

Library of Congress Control Number: 2010925514

...to the children of the world...

What is true?

A long time ago
it was true and everybody knew
that the earth was flat,
that the sun circles around the earth
and that a man cannot fly.

But today
it's true and everybody knows
that the earth is *round,*
that the earth circles around the *sun*
and that a man *can* fly—
well, at least in an airplane, or a rocket!

Does that mean
that what is true
is something that can change?

What is true?

If I tell you that snow is white
but you have never seen snow,
should you just believe me?

If I tell you that the stove is hot
but you have never touched a hot stove,
should you just believe me?

If I tell you that cheeseburgers
are not really good for you,
should you just believe me?

Should you believe
whatever anybody tells you is true?

Or should you find out for yourself
what is true?

Can something be true
even if you can't see it?

It's true that there are stars
up in the sky during the day,
even if you can't see them.

It's true that there are fish
in the ocean
even if you can't see them.

It's true that there are rabbits
in rabbit holes,
even if you can't see them.

But how can you know
that something is true,
if you can't see it?

To really know what is true,
maybe we have to *investigate!*

To *investigate* means
to find out for yourself
if something is true or not.

So, if you really want to know
if there are fish in the ocean,
maybe you can investigate
by diving into the ocean
to find out for yourself
if there are any fish down there.

If you really want to know
if snow is white,
maybe you can climb up a mountain
to see if that white stuff
at the top is really snow.

But if you want to know
if the stove is really hot,
do you really have to touch it?

When should we investigate
if something is true,
and when should we not?

Is what is true always as simple
as it sounds?

Firefighters fight fires,
dancers dance,
and owls *hoot*, right?
Those things sound simple
and true, right?

But firefighters also eat and sleep,
and watch TV
and do all kinds of other stuff too, right?

A dancer also walks and skips,
and jumps, right?

An owl *hoots*
but an owl also flies,
and eats mice, right?

Maybe what is true
is not always as simple
as it sounds.

Sometimes we say something
about somebody or something
that we think is true,
but maybe it's just our *opinion*.

Now an *opinion* is just what you believe
about somebody or something,
and any person can have an opinion—
but that opinion may just be true
for that person.

Maybe a friend says something about you
that is just his or her opinion
and that may not really be true—
but that may hurt you, right?

Or maybe you say something about a friend
that is just your opinion
and that may not really be true—
and that might hurt your friend, right?

So, maybe when we say something,
about somebody or something,
we should be real careful
to know what is true,
and what is just our opinion.

Sometimes we have to decide
what is true and what is *not* true,
and that can be very hard to do.

Like maybe you have a fight
with your friend at school,
and you blame your friend
for starting the fight,
and he blames *you!*

Well, how can we decide what is true
when two people *both* believe
that what each of them is saying is true?

Well, maybe your Mom or Dad,
or your teacher, or another grown-up
or even another kid,
can help you decide what is true.

But how do *they* know what is true?

Maybe if you slow down,
take a few breaths and listen real quietly,
deep inside yourself,
you will be able to hear and know
what is really true.

Should we believe what is true
just because a *million* people say
that something is true?

Suppose a *million* people say
that eating candy is good for kids.
Does that make it really true?

Suppose a *million* people say
that Santa Claus lives up in the North Pole.
Does that make it really true?

Suppose a *million* people say
that the Tooth Fairy is real,
and so is the bogeyman.
Does that make it really true?

What if a *million* people say
that you should not like
people with green skin because they eat bugs!
Does that make it really true?

Can a *million* people ever be wrong?

Can we change what is true
if we believe that by changing something
we can make it better for all of us?

Maybe it's true that a kid is a tattle-tale,
or that a kid is a bully,
or that a kid bites his or her nails—
and maybe because of those things,
you start not to like those kids.

But maybe a tattle-tale is really afraid of something,
maybe a bully is really angry about something,
and maybe a nail-biter is really worried about something.

So, maybe we can begin to understand
that those kids really need some help.

And maybe we can figure out
how to change things so that
we can make things better for all of us.

Maybe we can even change war to peace,
or polluted places to clean places,
and maybe we can even change
the sometimes not-so-nice things that we do
into nice things!

Sometimes we say something that is not true,
or that is not our opinion,
and that is called a *lie.*

Sometimes we lie in order to hide something
because we are afraid of what might happen to us
if somebody finds out what is true.

(Did you ever lie because you were afraid?)

Sometimes we lie to hurt somebody,
or to make ourselves feel important.

Sometimes we lie just a little bit
so as not to hurt somebody's feelings,
and that's called a *white* lie.

Sometimes a person tells so many lies
that he or she forgets what is true.

Maybe if we just say what is true,
even though we are afraid
of what might happen to us,
then maybe nothing bad will really happen.

Maybe most of the time
it's easier just to say what is true,
and *not* to lie—what do you think?

Maybe what is true
is just what is always happening—
right now!

What does *that* mean?

If you are breathing,
in and out, in and out,
that is what is true—
right now!

If you feel the cold winter air
blowing on your face,
that is what is true—
right now!

If you see some bright red roses
or hear some birds singing,
or taste some yummy ice cream,
that is what is true—
right now!

So, maybe what is true
is just what is always happening—
right now!

A long time ago a very wise person said
that what is true can be two different things
at the same time.
What did he mean by *that?*

Like, did you ever go to the beach
and make a sand castle with some wet sand?

What happens when the ocean
sends in a little wave
and washes away the sand castle?
Is it still a sand castle?

One minute it's true
that you have a sand castle,
but the next minute, it just goes back
to being the wet sand that it always was anyway.

So it was true that you had a sand castle
but it was also true
that all you had was really some wet sand.

That's an example of how what is true
can be two different things at the same time.

Can you think about two different things
that are true at the same time?

Is everything we see in a movie,
　　or watch on TV, or see in a commercial,
　　or play on a video game true?
　　Is everything we read true?

Is there really a *Super Hero*
who can beat up all the bad guys
and fly off the tops of buildings
and never get hurt?

Is there really a girl
who always has cool friends
and cool clothes,
and always gets to go anywhere she wants,
whenever she wants?

Maybe when we watch those movies,
or TV shows or commercials,
or play those video games,
or go on the internet
we have to think and decide carefully
about what is true, and about what is *not* true.

Why do you think it's important
to think about that one?

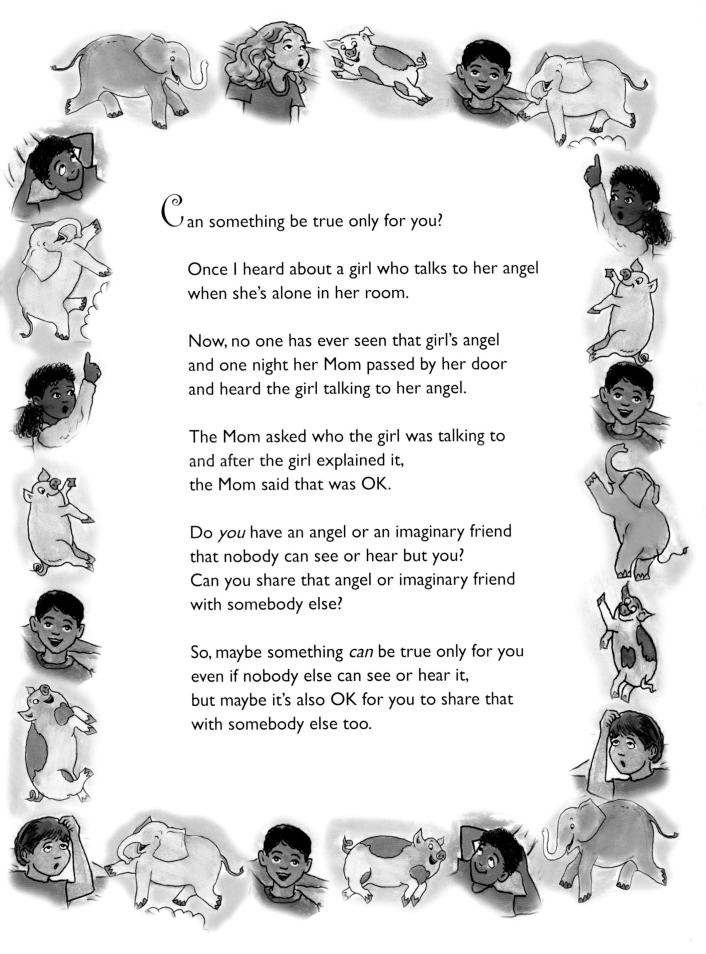

Can something be true only for you?

Once I heard about a girl who talks to her angel
when she's alone in her room.

Now, no one has ever seen that girl's angel
and one night her Mom passed by her door
and heard the girl talking to her angel.

The Mom asked who the girl was talking to
and after the girl explained it,
the Mom said that was OK.

Do *you* have an angel or an imaginary friend
that nobody can see or hear but you?
Can you share that angel or imaginary friend
with somebody else?

So, maybe something *can* be true only for you
even if nobody else can see or hear it,
but maybe it's also OK for you to share that
with somebody else too.

Can something be true
always, everywhere and forever?

We know that it's true that everything changes,
that flowers get old and die,
that dolls get left under the bed,
and that cars get broken and forgotten.

We know that it's true that mountains change,
that forests, rivers and oceans change.

But do we know anything that is true
always, everywhere and forever?

Maybe what is true,
always, everywhere and forever is *Love,*
or *Peace,* or *Respect* or that nice feeling we get
when we help people who need our help.

Maybe there are many other things
that are also true always, everywhere and forever—
if we just stop to think about them.

What is true?

Maybe what is true
is something that we can investigate,
on our own, or with some help from other people.

Maybe what is true
Is something that is always, everywhere and forever,
but maybe what is true also changes from time to time.

Maybe what is true can be two different things
at the same time.

Maybe what is true is sometimes different
for different people.

Maybe what is true
is what is always happening right now.

And maybe what is true
is a question that we can and should keep asking
our whole lives!